CW00643947

Physical and Physiological Analysis of Soya Seeds from the 2016/2017 Harvest

Larissa Dal Gallo Maschio
Paloma A. Sexto
Elisandra Urio

Physical and Physiological Analysis of Soya Seeds from the 2016/2017 Harvest

In the Northern Region of Rio Grande do Sul

ScienciaScripts

Imprint
Any brand names and product names mentioned in this book are subject to trademark, brand or patent protection and are trademarks or registered trademarks of their respective holders. The use of brand names, product names, common names, trade names, product descriptions etc. even without a particular marking in this work is in no way to be construed to mean that such names may be regarded as unrestricted in respect of trademark and brand protection legislation and could thus be used by anyone.

Cover image: www.ingimage.com

This book is a translation from the original published under ISBN 978-613-9-60775-4.

Publisher:
Sciencia Scripts
is a trademark of
Dodo Books Indian Ocean Ltd. and OmniScriptum S.R.L publishing group

120 High Road, East Finchley, London, N2 9ED, United Kingdom
Str. Armeneasca 28/1, office 1, Chisinau MD-2012, Republic of Moldova, Europe

ISBN: 978-620-7-30091-4

SUMMARY

CHAPTER 1

EXECUTOR

Larissa Dal Gallo Maschio, level IX Agronomy student at the Instituto de Desenvolvimento Educacional do Alto Uruguai - IDEAU, C ampus Getúlio Vargas - RS, e-mail: larissad.m@hotmail.com.

CHAPTER 2

GUIDE

Elisandra Andreia Urio, Me. Professor of Agronomy, Veterinary Medicine, Dentistry and Pedagogy at IDEAU College in Getúlio Vargas - RS.

E-mail: **elisandra-urio@ideau.com.br.**

CHAPTER 3

RESEARCH PROBLEM

In agricultural production, seed is considered a complete technology, as it expresses its full potential during its development, both productive and genetic. It is therefore important to preserve its physical and physiological characteristics, since despite all the technology available, in some regions production has been severely compromised due to seed deterioration, COSTA, (2001).

Seed viability is determined through tests that offer a series of advantages associated with a wide range of information. The provision of diagnostics is essential, as it is the determining factor for producers and can define the quality of a batch of seeds, knowing whether or not they will be suitable for cultivation. It is therefore necessary to determine the physical and physiological quality of soya beans harvested in the 2016/2017 season.

CHAPTER 4

OBJECTIVES

The following sections present the objectives of this project.

4.1 General objective

To assess the physical and physiological quality of soya beans from the 2016/2017 harvest.

4.2 Specific objectives

- Verify physical and physiological quality through mechanical damage tests;
- Evaluate the germination of the seeds of each cultivar, quantifying normal seedlings, abnormal seedlings and dormant seeds.
- Determine vigour by accelerated ageing in a BOD chamber;
- Determine the Thousand Seed Weight (MSW).

CHAPTER 5

BACKGROUND

In the quest to find high quality seeds and considering seed to be a complete agricultural technology, it is known that seed production has fluctuated due to the use of inferior quality seeds.

For this reason, maintaining the physical and physiological quality of seeds is extremely important and in some regions quality has been compromised by deterioration due to humidity, breakage, tegument rupture, mechanical damage and insect damage (COSTA, 2001). The quality of seeds is therefore guaranteed by analysing them according to standards set by the Ministry of Agriculture and Supply (MAPA). It is known that the final destination of these seeds is the field, which is why it is necessary to establish the stand for the farmer.

The emergence of seedlings in the field depends on the environmental conditions and these cannot be controlled, except if they are not in protected cultivation. To this end, tests must be carried out to efficiently identify consistent ways in which batches are more likely to develop in the field with the expected return (FILHO, 2001).

In view of the above, the results of this study can contribute important data on the physical and physiological quality of seeds analysed in the 2016/2017 harvest, providing producers with useful information that can be used on a daily basis when choosing cultivars, products and sowing methods.

CHAPTER 6

THEORETICAL FRAMEWORK

This chapter covers important theoretical aspects of soya cultivation and the subject of this project

6.1 HISTORY OF SOYA CULTIVATION

The soya bean, *Glycine max* (L.) Merrill, is one of Brazil's main export crops. It evolved when two wild species were domesticated and improved through natural crossbreeding in ancient China, more precisely in the Yangtze River region. In the second decade of the 20th century, soya began to attract interest due to the quantity of oils and proteins in its grains, arousing the interest of global industries, but the introduction of soya cultivation into the commercial market failed due to unfavourable climatic conditions for the development of the crop (EMBRAPA, 2004).

According to Embrapa (2004), the plant has a well-developed main root system with a large number of secondary roots that promote the survival of the crop, as well as being rich in nodules of *Rhizobium japonicum* bacteria that promote the fixation of atmospheric nitrogen. The soya bean, whose cultivated species is *Glycine max* (L.) Merrill, belongs to the dicotyledonous family of annual herbaceous legumes and the Papilionoides subfamily.

Brazil is the second largest producer of soya because it has a range of resources available, such as modernisation in mechanisation and the expansion of agricultural frontiers, contributing to the development of other crops and strengthening the Brazilian pig and poultry sector (DALLAGANOL, 2000).

Soya plays the role of one of the main oilseeds produced and consumed with great importance for both animal and vegetable consumption, but faces

7

structural challenges related to the logistics chain where the use of roads for transport predominates without the viability of exploring waterways, which increases the cost of transporting production, (SILVA et al 2005).

Soya is widely commercialised and distributed internally and externally, bringing together thousands of companies, from small input dealers to large transnationals. This is due to the solid markets established for its by-products (soya meal and oil). Soya meal is a fundamental input for animal nutrition, particularly for poultry, pigs and confined cattle. With the increase in consumption of animal protein, the consumption of soya meal has gradually grown, especially in meat-producing countries such as China and Brazil. China has adopted the strategy of importing grains for internal processing to obtain bran, rather than importing the derived product. As a result, the Asian country is the destination of more than 60% of the world's soya beans exports. This makes China one of the main players in the global soya agribusiness, and it is largely responsible for the expansion of the commodity market (Krzyzanowski, 2016).

Given the extensive development of soya cultivation, Brazil is keeping pace with scientific advances and making technologies available to the production sector. Mechanisation and the creation of cultivars adapted to different regions have led to an increase in demand for soya in recent years, and identifying solutions to the main factors responsible for losses in the harvesting method are factors that promote this progress, although there are still some factors that limit productivity (FREITAS et al., 2011).

With the largest cultivated area among national crops, soya is the biggest consumer of seeds, fertilisers and pesticides in Brazilian agriculture, which are used in more than 200,000 rural establishments. As well as soya being the main demander of seeds among the crops indicated, the evolution of its demand over the period is greater than the quantities demanded for seeds of all the other commodities, which shows that soya is fundamental to boosting this link in the Brazilian agricultural production chain (INDICADORES IBGE, 2006).

Brazil is a food producer and exporter, with soya being one of the main agribusiness products. The market for differentiated grains is expanding and demands are for the characterisation of the grains and the definition of the technological quality produced, which is necessary to secure current and conquer new markets. Better quality soya beans could lead to commercial crops with high yields and high commercial standards, promoting greater competitiveness and gains for the soya production chain. The definition of quality must take into account various factors such as the genetics of the soya, the amount of defects and damage at harvest, the physical, physiological, sanitary and purity characteristics of the seeds, which characterise the quality of the seed and the technological suitability of the grain.

With the growing enrichment of Brazilian agriculture, there have been a number of changes in the production process. Among agricultural inputs, good quality seed plays a fundamental role in the production system, which tends to improve quantitative and qualitative standards (COSTA et al., 2001). Seed deterioration is directly related to physical and physiological changes which, as a consequence, can lead to plant death, as well as directly interfering with germination, vigour, viability and deterioration due to humidity, causing a large number of losses due to mechanical damage, rupture of the seed coat and major losses in seed quality standards

9

(FRANÇA, 1984).

6.2 Seed Physiological Quality

Seed is considered to be the main agricultural input, as it brings all the genetic characteristics to the field, attributing all the physical, physiological and sanitary quality that the grain possesses. The competitiveness of the market has made investment in seed quality increasingly efficient, contributing to the stabilisation and success of the stand and the profitable production of a well-established crop (BARROS, MARCOS FILHO, 2002).

For seed to be considered high quality, it must have characteristics such as a high vigour rate, germination and health, guaranteeing physical purity without containing weed seeds (KRZYANOWSKI, 2004).

The physiological quality of seeds is determined by their vigour and germination. The composition of the seed is the limiting factor for the plant to germinate, its morphological structure determines its sensitivity to external factors, which makes it difficult to obtain seeds with germination capacity and vigour (PESKE, 2012).

Seed production requires knowledge that includes choosing the area, using recommended cultivars, sowing on different dates, monitoring vegetative growth, cultural treatments, phytosanitary treatments, deciding when to harvest and cleaning machinery, harvesters and transport lorries, all of which must be precisely followed. Harvesting is a considerable stage in the soya production method, mainly due to the risks to which the crop will be subjected (EMBRAPA, 2002).

Some of the factors involved in soya bean seed quality are mechanical damage, as these seeds are very sensitive to this type of damage because the vital parts of the embryonic axis (radicle, hypocotyl and plumule) are

10

located under a seed coat that is not very thick and offers little protection (FRANÇA NETO & HENNING, 1984). The susceptibility of the seed coat to mechanical damage is of fundamental importance in determining seed quality, as it is associated with genetic variability (CARBONELL, 1991).

The quality of soya bean seed is made up of four pillars: 1. Physiological quality, representing seed with high vigour and germination, resulting in adequate seedling emergence in the field; 2. Genetic quality, being genetically pure, representing the cultivar you want to sow, without varietal mixtures; 3. Sanitary quality, comprising seed free of other weed seeds and pathogens, be they fungi, viruses, nematodes or bacteria; 4. Physical quality, comprising pure seed, free of inert material such as contaminants, plant fragments, insects, clods and other impurities.

Environmental stresses, which result in premature plant death or forced ripening, can cause a severe reduction in crop productivity, as well as the production of greenish seeds: root diseases, such as fusariosis, stem diseases, such as stem canker, and leaf diseases, such as Asian rust; intense insect attacks, especially sucking insects; water deficit (drought or summer) during the final stages of grain filling and ripening, especially if associated with high temperatures; and the occurrence of intense frost, which can result in the premature death of the plant (FRANÇA-NETO et al., 2012). Greenish soya beans have affected vigour and germination, consequences that are accentuated as the storage period passes. The higher the percentage of greenish seed in a batch of seed, the lower its quality (PÁDUA et al., 2007).

The genetic purity of soya beans is another important factor, as it is also one of the components of their quality. When a soya grower buys soya beans, he wants a guarantee that the seeds he is buying are actually from the cultivar he is interested in. It is important that the seed is genetically pure, free from mixtures with seeds from other cultivars, seeds from cultivated, wild and harmful species.

Another factor that can affect the performance of soya beans is the action of bedbugs, which cause lesions that compromise seed quality. According to Panizzi (1979), the period that corresponds to the incidence of these insects is the stage of development and pod filling.

Insect pests of stored grains, which until a few years ago did not cause severe damage during storage, now characterise a problem that causes damage and losses to the production sector, making it necessary to monitor them as they can compromise seed quality.

Seed quality is the result of the sum of physical, physiological, health and genetic attributes. Genetic quality or varietal purity is very important, as it is through this that the farmer will be guaranteed that the crop will be established with the cultivar recommended for it. In this way, the greater the genetic purity, the greater the guarantee of adequate crop performance. Since 2013, Brazilian legislation has no longer made it compulsory to test for other cultivars (varietal mixtures) when carrying out the purity analysis of soya beans, through the publication of IN 45 of September 2013 (BRASIL, 2013). Since then, control of the genetic identity of the commercialised cultivar has been guaranteed in field inspections, according to methodologies and standards established by legislation (GREGG et al., 2011).

6.3 Seed certification and quality control

The certification system guarantees quality standards in terms of origin, physical and genetic purity and physiological and sanitary qualities. This is done to meet the demands of seed producers.

Under the certification system, the process of renewing seed classes is carried out systematically. Adopting the system in the seed production programme avoids the use of inferior seed classes, which has contributed to an increase in the percentage of mixed cultivars, resulting in a lower quality signal product (Henning, 2008).

The mixture of cultivars can affect the soya bean crop in several ways, such as: increased harvest losses due to the lack of uniformity in plant maturity at harvest time; the quality of the grain for industrial use can be affected by the presence of substandard plants due to the mixture of green, highly moist and burnt grains (Costg, 2008).

Seed is an extremely useful tool for spreading technology. The lack of class renewal in seed production can delay farmers' access to the new cultivars distributed by the certification system. These new cultivars could contribute to new genetic advances, such as resistance to diseases, better organoleptic quality of the grain and high yield potential (Henning, 2008).

6.3.1 Use of quality seeds.

Seed certification is the production process controlled by a competent public or private body, which guarantees that the seed has been produced in such a way that its genetic origin can be known with certainty and that it fulfils pre-established physiological, health and physical conditions. Certification is an important component of the seed industry, since it operates at all stages, taking part in production, processing, commercialisation and also providing services to farmers. It is the only method that makes it possible to maintain the seed's varietal identity in an open market. By controlling generations, it allows the seeds of superior cultivars to maintain their genetic purity and all their qualitative characteristics after being placed on the market by the Breeders, (Levien, 2014).

Five reasons why you should use certified seed to sow your crops:

- Because certified seed has generation control, i.e. you know how many times the cultivar has been multiplied after being released by the breeder who developed it. This is a guarantee of the cultivar's origin. In other words, you plant the cultivar that you really planned for your crop. It is important to control/limit generations, as it has been proven that, in most cases, the seed of autogamous species begins to degenerate after the fifth generation. In other words, after this period the cultivar doesn't express all its potential, because natural crosses and mixtures with other cultivars have occurred, leading mainly to yield losses.
- Because certified seed has a guaranteed quality standard. This standard is determined by samples collected by the Certifying Body and analysed in a Seed Analysis Laboratory accredited by the Ministry of Agriculture, Livestock and Supply - MAPA. This guarantees the physical and physiological quality of the seed. In other words, you buy the cultivar and have the guarantee that it will germinate and not infest your crop. This can lead to higher yields and consequently greater profitability for your crop.
- Because certified seed has the guarantee of the Seed Producer who

produced it, through the certificate and the invoice that accompanies it. This is a product guarantee. In other words, if you have a problem with the seed, you'll know where to turn to claim your rights.

- Because certified seed is legal seed. This is security. In other words, you're using seed from a cultivar registered with MAPA, backed by the Seed Law. With this seed you have access to credit and Proagro cover.

- Because certified seed is the vehicle for introducing the latest advances in plant breeding. This is technological innovation. You will be using seed from a cultivar that has been evaluated and has demonstrated its qualities under our conditions (Certifying Body).

Source: Fundação Pró-sementes.

6.4 Seed Sampling for Laboratory Analysis

Seed analysis was devised and has been continually improved with the aim of providing information on the quality of seeds to be used for sowing purposes, in an attempt to avoid some of the risks to which they are subject in agriculture (MAPA, 1992). The Rules for Seed Analysis (RAS) are intended to provide information on seed quality, as well as serving as a guide for various fronts within the olive sector, from farmers to official and seed production laboratories.

One of the most important RAS rules is sampling. Sampling makes it possible to study the relationships between a population and the samples taken from it. Sampling is fundamental at all stages of seed quality assessment, from sourcing, production, the receiving process, processing, analysis to Trade Inspection, since the characteristics of a volume or batch of seeds are based on the sampling carried out according to previously described procedures.

The average sample received by the laboratory usually needs to be reduced to one or more working samples to be used in the various determinations. This reduction can be carried out either mechanically or manually. Regardless of the method used to obtain the working sample, this stage must be carried out with great care and attention so that it can truly represent the batch of seeds being analysed. The combination of several single samples will make up the average sample, which will be homogenised and sent to the seed laboratory for analysis (Table 1.0). The purity, moisture content and viability of the batch are obtained by analysing the working sample.

Table 1.0: Maximum lot size, minimum weight of the average sample and working sample established for wheat and soya.

Culture	Maximum Lot Size (Kg)	Minimum weight in grams	
		Sample Average	Analysis Purity
Soya	30.000	1 000	500
Wheat	30.000	1.000	120

Source: Brazil, 2009.

6.5 Using cultivars that produce high quality seed

The success of a soya production programme depends on the use of suitable cultivars. As well as having good yield potential, cultivars must produce high quality seed, which will ensure adequate plant stands. In Brazil, there are several breeding programmes that produce cultivars with better genetic seed quality (França Neto & Krzyzanowski, 2004).

In addition to this line of breeding for seed quality, other work also includes selection for high seed quality using the modified methodology of accelerated ageing and controlled deterioration. There are other characteristics and methods that can be used in breeding programmes to improve soybean seed quality, including other properties of the seed coat, such as impermeability to water, colour, the presence of a waxy epidermis and the characteristics of its pores, the semi-permeability of the pod walls, resistance to fungi, tolerance to wrinkling resulting from exposure to high temperatures during the grain filling phase, and seed size.

6.6 Mechanical Damage Test

According to Krzyzanowski et al. (2004), mechanical damage is a factor that limits the production of soya beans of adequate quality. The most critical period corresponding to the seed production phases is harvesting and processing, because the impacts caused by the tracking mechanisms during the process cause irreversible damage to the seed. Costa et al. (2003), cites that breaks and rupture of the tegument arise due to mechanical damage to the seeds and directly affect the physiological quality of the seeds.

The seed production process requires technologies that include area selection, the use of recommended varieties, sowing at set times, monitoring vegetative development, cultivation, plant health treatments, determining the ideal time to harvest and cleaning machinery, harvesters and transport lorries, which must be strictly followed. Harvesting is an important stage in the soya production process, mainly due to the risks to which the crop intended for seed production is subject (Embrapa, 2002).

Mechanical harvesting and processing are the main sources of mechanical damage to seeds. During harvesting, the seed is particularly susceptible to immediate or latent mechanical damage (Paiva et al., 2000). In this case, mechanical damage occurs at the time of threshing, i.e. when considerable forces are applied to the seeds in order to separate them from

17

the structure that contains them. It essentially occurs as a result of the impacts received from the threshing cylinder as they pass through the concave. The seed in the harvester is a static body against which a metal body, the bars of the threshing cylinder, moves (Carvalho and Nakagawa, 2000). For mechanical harvesting of soya beans, the market has harvesters with transverse cylinder and concave threshing systems and, recently, axial flow harvesters, which can produce different effects on the physiological quality of the material to be used as seed (Marcos and Mielii, 2003).

The sodium hypochlorite test provides rapid results for mechanical damage to seeds, showing the presence of tegument ruptures (KRZYZANOWSKI et al., 2004). This test is used both when the seed is received and along the processing line to assess mechanical damage caused by the equipment.

6.7 Germination and vigour

According to the RAS, the seed germination test is the emergence and development of essential structures, showing their ability to produce a normal plant under suitable field conditions.

According to Borges & Rena (1993), germination can be considered the growth of the embryonic axis, which is paralysed during maturation, i.e. it is the phase that corresponds, from a physiological point of view, to the exit from rest to the intensification of metabolic activities.

One of the factors that greatly influences germination is soaking. According to Toledo & Filho (1977), water influences germination by acting on the seed coat, softening and favouring the penetration of oxygen and allowing soluble nutrients to be transferred throughout the seed.

The appropriate temperature for germination, according to Bewley

(1994), is on average 20 to 30°C. The incidence of light breaks the dormancy of those seeds that may be temperature-dependent.

Evaluating seed vigour has become a routine tool for seed producers, as it allows them to assess physiological quality, distinguishing between high and low vigour batches, managing or eliminating less vigorous seeds and reducing the possibility of losses (FILHO, 1999).

6.7.1 Ungerminated seeds

For a seed to germinate, it needs to be in suitable conditions in terms of water, temperature and environment. According to the RAS (2009), ungerminated seeds are classified as:

- Hard seeds: these are seeds that have spent a longer period of time without absorbing water and have not become hardened due to the fact that the integument has not been impermeable to water, which is a type of dormancy.

- Dormant seeds: These are seeds that experience a delay in germination, that even when subjected to favourable conditions of development and even if they have soaked, do not germinate.

- Dead seeds: seeds that at the end of the test have not germinated, are not hard or dormant, and are often softened, attacked by micro-organisms and show no sign of starting to germinate.

- Empty seeds: seeds that are completely empty or contain only some residual tissue.

- Seeds without an embryo: seeds that contain an embryo in formation or gametophytic tissue in which there is apparently no embryonic cavity or embryo.

- Seeds damaged by insects: seeds that contain larvae or show evidence of insect attack affecting their germination capacity.

6.7.2 Normal seedlings

A normal seedling is one that has well-developed essential structures and the ability to germinate under favourable field conditions. A root system with long secondary roots, a large number of absorbent hairs, a well-developed aerial part and cotyledons are the structures that will give the plant the capacity to develop (BRASIL, 2006).

6.7.3 Abnormal seedlings

It does not have the potential to continue its development and give rise to normal plants, even if subjected to favourable field conditions. Damaged seedlings: Any essential structure missing or so damaged that proportional growth cannot occur. Deformed seedlings: with poor development, or physiological disorders, or with deformed or disproportionate essential structures. Deteriorated seedlings: with any of their essential structures badly infected or badly deteriorated, as a result of a primary infection, of the seed itself, which jeopardises its normal growth, (BRASIL, 2006).

6.8 Weight of a Thousand Seeds

The weight of a thousand seeds is calculated to determine the sowing density and establish the weight of the working sample. The working sample will be taken in the proportion of "Pure Seeds". This information allows the size of the seeds, their state of maturity and health to be verified (BRASIL, 2006).

CHAPTER 7

MATERIAL AND METHODS

7.1 Experiment

The evaluations were carried out at the CEBTEC Agro Seed Laboratory, located in the city of Mato Castelhano -RS, latitude 28°16'42" south and longitude 52°11'30" west.

7.2 Experimental design

We used 20 different soya cultivars, classified as the most widely used in the region, as shown in Table 2. The experimental design used was completely randomised (DIC), with four replications for each cultivar.

Table 2: Soya cultivars to be used in the tests:

CULTIVARS
1- 69I59 IPRO
2- 5855 RSF IPRO
3- NS 5959 IPRO
4- TMG 71761 RSF IPRO
5- 50I70 RSF IPRO
6- 69I69 RSF IPRO
7- 68I70 RSF IPRO
8- TMG 7062 IPRO
9- 6863 RSF
10- NS 6700 IPRO
11- NS 6535 IPRO
12- 7166 RSF IPRO
13- NS 6209
14- M5730 IPRO
15- NA5909 RG
16- 6968 RSF
17- 58I60 RSF IPRO
18- M5947 IPRO
19- ACTIVE BMX RR
20- TMG 7062

7.3 Evaluations and analyses

The evaluations were conducted as follows:

To assess the physical quality of the seeds, the mechanical damage test was carried out. To do this, 200 seeds were selected from each sample and divided into 4 repetitions, i.e. each repetition had 50 seeds each. These seeds were placed in a solution of sodium hypochlorite and water in a 1/1 ratio, where they remained for 10 minutes, as shown in Figure 1. The seeds were then assessed to see which ones had soaked. This process consists of the absorption of water by the seed cells, thus causing an increase in volume and weight in each of the repetitions. According to Vaughan (1982), if the percentage of soaked seeds is greater than 10%, the seed is very damaged and adjustments need to be made to the harvester and equipment, as well as to the processing.

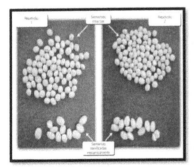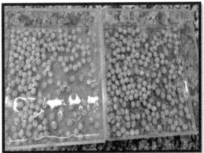

Figure 1- Mechanical damage test with sodium hypochlorite on soya beans. Photo: MASCHIO, L., Seed Analysis Laboratory, CEBTEC Agro, Mato Castelhano, 2017.

- Germination assessment: 400 seeds of each cultivar were used for this test, chosen at random with 4 replicates of 100 seeds. The test was carried out on a Germitest® paper roll. Four sheets of paper were used, two under the seeds and two covering them, as shown in Figure 2. The humidity of soya substrate paper is twice the weight of the paper, i.e. the total weight of the papers used was multiplied by two, giving the result of the amount of distilled water used to wet the sheets of paper. It is worth emphasising that no treated seeds were used for this test. The seeds were counted using a seed counter, where the seeds were evenly distributed over the paper. The distance between the seeds established by the RAS is 15 cm. The replicates were grouped together and secured with rubber ties in a plastic bag to keep the rolls moist. For germination, the samples were placed in a germination chamber at 25°C and a 12-hour photoperiod for 5 days.

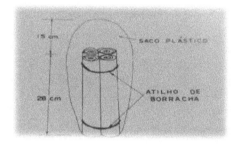

Figura 2: Packing the germination rolls with plastic bags to carry out the tests. Source: Krzyzanowoski et al., 1991

For accelerated ageing vigour, a single layer of seeds was placed on a screen in a gerbox with 40 ml of distilled water inside (Figure 3). The samples were kept in a BOD (Biochemical Oxygen Demand) germination chamber with relative humidity control, at a temperature of 42°C, for a period of 48 hours. After the ageing period, the seeds were put to germinate, going through the same germination process described above, and the assessment was carried out 5 days after sowing.

Figura 3: Accelerated ageing vigour test. Photo: MASCHIO, L., Seed Analysis Laboratory, CEBTEC Agro, Mato Castelhano, 2017.

The assessment of normal and abnormal seedlings in the germination test is the average of the four repetitions and is the sum of the percentages of normal seedlings, abnormal seedlings, hard, dormant and dead seeds. Figure 4 shows a comparison of seeds that germinated correctly and seeds that did not continue to develop into normal seedlings, with no root system, aerial part or cotyledons.

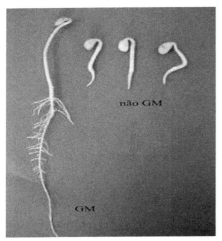

Figura 4: - Comparison between normal (GM - germinated) and abnormal (non-GM - non-germinated) seedlings. Source: (Bewley & Black, 1994).

Thousand-seed weight: 8 replicates of 100 seeds from each sample were selected for this assessment. As the weight of a thousand seeds in a sample varies according to the water content of the seeds, the degree of humidity was determined. The eight samples were then weighed using an experimental precision balance and the values obtained from the weighings were calculated using the thousand seed weight formula:

Seed weight inil (PAIS) = $\dfrac{\textbf{sample weight x 1,000}}{\textbf{n" total number of seeds}}$

Because the seeds were chosen in the proportion of pure seeds, the variance, standard deviation and coefficient of variation of the values obtained from the weighings were calculated.

The test to analyse the statistical data for all the evaluations was carried out using the System for the Analysis and Separation of Means in Agricultural Experiments (SASM-Agri) using the Tukey method with a 5% probability of error.

CHAPTER 8

RESULTS AND DISCUSSION

After all the analyses were carried out, the results computed and the statistical tests performed, the following results were obtained.

In relation to the mechanical damage data, cracks and splits were detected superficially and were easy to observe with the naked eye, but this test does not reveal internal mechanical damage, which requires further tests. It is worth emphasising that within the seed production process, mechanical damage is one of the most important causes of reduced seed quality. The data obtained when the samples were subjected to the mechanical damage test (Table 3) shows the following results:

Table 3 - Average mechanical damage results

Mechanical damage test	
Cultivar	**Average**
Treatment 11	14,5 a
Treatment 9	8,25 b
Treatment 4	6.5 bc
Treatment 8	6.5 bc
Treatment 18	6.5 bc
Treatment 20	6.25 bc
Treatment 3	4.25 bcd
Treatment 12	4.25 bcd
Treatment 17	4.25 bcd
Treatment 01	3.75 bcd
Treatment 7	3.5 bcd
Treatment 15	3.25 bcd
Treatment 10	3 bcd
Treatment 5	2.75 cd

Treatment	
Treatment 14	2.75 cd
Treatment 6	2.5 cd
Treatment 19	1.75 cd
Treatment 13	1.5 cd
Treatment 16	1.5 cd
Treatment 2	0,5 d

CV: 45.8

*Numbers followed by the same letters in the column do not differ statistically by Tukey's test at 5%.

Although the samples showed different levels of damage, the detrimental effects of damage on seed quality can be seen most strongly in treatments 11 and 9, where the cultivars showed the greatest amount of damaged seeds, differing from the other cultivars that had lower levels of mechanical damage, such as treatment 2. This shows that soya beans are very sensitive to this type of damage and that the consequence of the impact is one of the main causes of reduced quality.

Mechanical damage to seeds is visible or immediate and invisible or latent. Immediate damage is easily characterised by the observation of broken integuments, separated and/or broken cotyledons with the naked eye, while latent damage involves microscopic cracks and/or abrasions or internal damage to the embryo, under which germination may not be immediately affected, but the vigour, storage potential and performance of the seed in the field are reduced (FRANÇA- NETO; HENNING, 1984).

Many authors have highlighted the genetic variability that exists in soya beans in terms of seed resistance to mechanical damage (AGRAWAL & MENON, 1974; STANWAY, 1978; KRZYZANOWWSKI et al., 1989), as well as methodologies for assessing this damage (PAULSEN et al., 1981;

27

FRANÇA NETO et al., 1988). However, little is known about the methodologies capable of selecting soya genotypes with seeds resistant to mechanical damage. Kueneman (1989) suggested the use of the "drop test" as a selection methodology for soya beans, in view of its use in bean seeds in the United States.

8.1 Germination

According to Brasil (2009), seed germination in a laboratory test is the emergence and development of the essential structures of the embryo, demonstrating its aptitude for producing a normal plant under favourable field conditions, although field conditions are variable and can be adverse. Germination and vigour tests (Figure 5) are essential in seed quality control, with the aim of identifying batches that are more or less likely to perform well in the field or during storage.

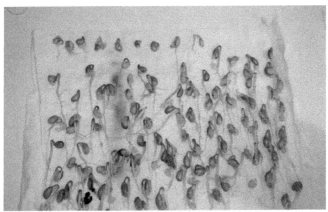

Figure 5: Germination test seedlings on Germitest paper roll - Photo: PIRAN, T., Seed Analysis and Certification Laboratory - CEBTEC AGRO - Mato Castelhano/ RS

After five days of germination, normal seedlings, abnormal seedlings and dead seeds were counted according to the evaluation criteria established in the Rules for Seed Analysis (BRASIL, 2009), with the results expressed as a percentage in Table 4.

Table 4- Results of the germination test averages.

Germination Test	
Treatment 4	96,5 a
Treatment 5	96,5 a
Treatment 14	96,5 a
Treatment 19	96,5 a
Treatment 9	96 a
Treatment 20	96 a
Treatment 2	95,5 a
Treatment 17	95,5 a
Treatment 18	95,5 a
Treatment 13	95.25 ab
Treatment 1	95 ab
Treatment 7	95 ab
Treatment 15	95 ab
Treatment 3	94 ab
Treatment 8	93.5 ab
Treatment 6	93.25 ab
Treatment 10	93 ab
Treatment 12	92.25 ab
Treatment 11	91.25 ab
Treatment 16	89.75 b

Cv: 2.25%

*Numbers followed by the same letters in the column do not differ statistically by the Tukey test at 5%.

The germination test carried out under favourable conditions and in a controlled environment allows seed lots to germinate completely and quickly. The statistical analysis did not show any significant differences in the germination of the different seed lots. However, the soya seeds from treatment 4, classified in sieve 6.0, had the highest percentage of normal seedlings and consequently the lowest percentage of abnormal seedlings in this test. As can be seen from the results presented above, no batch showed an unsatisfactory result, with good germination performance, and no batch was lost.

Hampton & Tekrony (1995) observed that the greatest limitation of the germination test is its inability to detect differences in physiological potential between lots with high germination, indicating the need to complement this information with the results of vigour tests. Furthermore, the size of the seeds probably does not influence the germination percentage, but it does influence vigour.

8.2 Vigour

The analysis of vigour contributes to a direct relationship with the initial growth of seedlings and their ability to accumulate biomass. The accelerated ageing test is recognised as one of the most widely used for assessing the physiological potential of seeds of various species, providing information with a high degree of consistency (TEKRONY, 1995). The results for the accelerated ageing test are shown in Table 5.

All batches of seeds were subjected to moisture content determination. Once the seeds had undergone accelerated ageing, the germination test was started on Germitest paper to assess the vigour of each batch of seeds. At the end of the test, on the fifth day after planting, the seedlings were quantified and the vigour was assessed (Figure 6).

Table 5: Results of the accelerated ageing test averages

Accelerated Ageing Test	
Treatment 14	94 a
Treatment 19	94 a
Treatment 15	93 ab
Treatment 4	92.75 bc
Treatment 13	92.75 bc
Treatment 9	92 bcd
Treatment 18	92 bcd
Treatment 20	92 bcd

Treatment 5	91.75 cdf
Treatment 17	91 def
Treatment 12	90.75 effg
Treatment 2	90.5 fg
Treatment 1	89.75 gh
Treatment 7	89.75 gh
Treatment 3	89,25 h
Treatment 6	87,75 i
Treatment 10	87,25 i
Treatment 16	86 j
Treatment 8	85,75 j
Treatment 11	84,25 k

CV: 3.29%

*Numbers followed by the same letters in the column do not differ statistically by the Tukey test at 5%.

Figure 6: Accelerated ageing test on soya beans. Photo: MASCHIO, L., Seed Analysis Laboratory, CEBTEC Agro, Mato Castelhano, 2017.

It can be seen that no batch failed, but some showed a reduced percentage of vigour, showing that all the seed batches obtained satisfactory results. This test combines high temperatures and high relative humidity, which probably led to a marked increase in seed metabolism.

One possible explanation could be that the larger seeds, because they had greater amounts of reserves and were also more available for metabolic processes, had a greater capacity to generate normal seedlings.

Therefore, seedlings from small or lighter seeds showed less growth of the aerial and root parts, less accumulation of dry phytomass and were less vigorous than seedlings from large or heavier seeds, corroborating the observations made by Carvalho & Nakagawa (2000) and Aguiar et al. (2001). In this way, the results show us that larger seeds generally provide better physiological performance, where the size or mass of the seeds reflected the content of reserve tissues available for the development of the seedling, directly interfering with its growth and initial vigour.

8.3 Mass of a thousand seeds

Seed size is conceptualised as a genetically determined varietal characteristic whose phenotypic expression is little influenced by the environment and should therefore not be considered a limiting factor for seed propagation, except when it is very different from the average of the majority of seeds in the batch (GIOMO, 2003) (Figure 7). There is a belief among farmers that crops generated by larger seeds have better yields due to the greater amount of reserve tissue in them. Table 6 shows the results for thousand-seed mass.

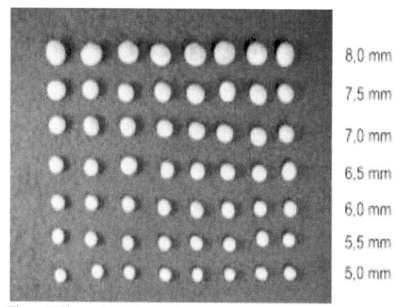

Figure 7: Size variation in soya beans sorted on a circular hole sieve.

Photo: KRZYZANOWSKI, F. C, 2008, Londrina PR.

Table 6: Thousand-seed mass according to sieve size and seed moisture content.

	Thousand Seed Pasta		
Cultivar	Sieve	PMS	Humidity
Treatment 1	6,5	186,5	13,5%
Treatment 2	5,75	152,7	13,3%
Treatment 3	6,0	163,2	13,4%
Treatment 4	6,0	155,8	13,3%
Treatment 5	6,0	161,1	13,4%
Treatment 6	6,5	188,7	13,2%
Treatment 7	6,25	182,0	13,3%
Treatment 8	6,25	204,0	13,4%
Treatment 9	6,0	162,4	13,3%
Treatment 10	6,5	184,8	13,0%
Treatment 11	5,75	159,0	13,3%
Treatment 12	6,75	204,9	13,1%
Treatment 13	6,0	164,3	13,1%
Treatment 14	5,75	150,1	13,3%
Treatment 15	6,5	184,2	13,4%
Treatment 16	5,5	150,8	13,1%
Treatment 17	7,0	226,9	13,2%
Treatment 18	5,75	152,7	13,2%
Treatment 19	6,5	184,4	13,4%

| Treatment 20 | 6,75 | 192,3 | 13,2% |

Source: MASCHIO, L. - Seed Analysis Laboratory- Cebtec Agro- Mato Castelhano/ RS 2017.

With regard to the average values for the mass of a thousand seeds, there were significant differences between the size classes, where the seeds with the highest mass were found among the seeds in the largest size classes (seeds classified in the 6.0 and 7.0 mm sieves).

The size and density of seeds do not influence their ability to germinate, but they do influence their vigour. Most research has shown that large seeds, because they contain a greater amount of reserve substances, germinate better than small seeds, have a higher emergence rate at greater depths and the plants they produce are heavier and more vigorous (CARVALHO; NAKAGAWA, 2000).

Seed size and its relationship with physiological potential have been contradictory issues in the work carried out by numerous researchers. According to Mcdonald Jr (1975), seed size evaluates the morphological aspects possibly associated with vigour. Ávila et al. (2005) working with turnip and cabbage seeds found significant differences when comparing seeds of different sizes.

However, Andrade et al. (1997), in maize, found no differences between the vigour of large and small seeds. Aguiar et al. (2001) found that there was no significant difference in the vigour of smaller sunflower seeds as soon as they were stored; however, after six months of storage, the smaller seeds showed less vigour when compared to the larger seeds.

There was a stratification of size classes into higher and lower physiological potential, with a predominance of significantly higher values for the larger seeds (classified in sieves with 6.75 mm holes) compared to the smaller seeds (classified in sieves with 5.0 mm holes), indicating the significant effect of size and significant reductions in vigour as seed size decreases. These results correlate with the vigour and germination tests carried out.

As mentioned above and according to BRASIL, (2009), the weight of a thousand seeds varies with the water content of the seeds. For this reason, the seed moisture content was determined, which showed that all batches of seeds had a similar percentage of moisture, which shows that both had little difference in water content. Dry seeds, i.e. those with a water content below 12%, tend to show immediate mechanical damage, characterised by cracks, splits and breakage. Seeds above 14% are more susceptible to latent mechanical damage, i.e. internal damage that is generally not visible to the naked eye.

CHAPTER 9

CONCLUSION

Through this study, even knowing that the cultivars used did not come from saved seeds and that no batch of seeds failed, it can be seen how important it is to use quality seeds, both in terms of germination characteristics and high vigour rates. High quality seeds result in strong, vigorous, well-developed seedlings that establish themselves in different soil and climate conditions. In addition, the use of high quality seeds guarantees an adequate plant population, greater speed of emergence and plant development, clearly demonstrating the fundamental importance of using quality seeds of known origin.

Finally, it is worth highlighting the importance of using cultivars with high germination power and vigour, as well as storing them in suitable packaging and at the ideal humidity point for storage, avoiding damage to the seed and preventing the spread of storage fungi and bacteria, so that batches are not condemned and seeds are suitable for planting and consequently high yield rates, large plant populations, with superior numbers of pods and quantity of grain per pod.

CHAPTER 10

SCHEDULE OF ACTIVITIES

The activities carried out to realise the project are described in the table below.

Table 1: Timetable of activities.

ACTIVITIES	F	M	A	M	J	J	A	S	O	N	D
Choice of topic and supervisor	■										
Meetings with the supervisor		■	■	■	■						
Literature review			■	■							
Drawing up the project		■	■	■							
Delivery of the research project											
Data collection and research		■	■	■							
Revision and final delivery of the work						■	■	■	■		
Presentation of the work to a panel											■
Start of data collection							■	■			

Source: The author

CHAPTER 11

BUDGET

Expenditure on material resources for the realisation of the project is described in the table below.

Table 2: Budget.

DETAILED PROJECT BUDGET - MATERIAL RESOURCES			
MATERIAL FOR CONTINUOUS USE			
Material Description	Quantity	Value (unit - in reais)	Total R$
Camera	1	990,00	990,00
Notebook	1	1.300,00	1.300,00
Subtotal	2	2.290,00	2.290,00
CONSUMABLES			
Material Description	Quantity	Value (unit - in reais)	Total R$
Germitest paper	360	0,25	90,00
Plastic bags	6	0,80	4,80
Rubber grip	200	0,10	20,00
Disposable cups	100	0,20	10,00
Subtotal	666	1,60	124,80
SERVICES: (copying, binding, graphic printing)			
Material Description	Quantity	Value (unit - in reais)	Total R$
Copying and binding	3	16,00	48,00

REFERENCES

AGRAWAL, PK.; MENON, S.K. Lignin content and seed coat thickness in relation to seed coat cracking in soybean. Seed Research, v.2, p.64-66, 1974.

BARROS, A.C.S.A.; PESKE, S.T. Typologies and marketing mix of wheat and soya seed companies in Rio Grande do Sul. Revista Brasileira de Sementes, v.24, n.1, p.81-90, 2002. DOI: 10.1590/S0101-31222002000100012

BEWLEY, J. D.; BLACK, M. Seeds: physiology of development and germination. 2. Ed. New York: Plenun Press, 2003. 445 p.

BORGES, E.E.L; CASTRO, J , L. D; BORGES R.C.G. Physiological evaluation of cedar seeds submitted to premature ageing. **Brazilian Seed Journal**. Brasilia, v12, n.1. p56-62, 2004.
BORGES, E. E. L.; RENA, A. B. Seed germination In: AGUIAR, I. B.; PINARODRIGUES, F. M. C.; FIGLIOLIA, M. B. (Coord.). Tropical forest seeds. Brasília: ABRATES, 2004. p. 83 - 135

BRAZIL. Normative Instruction No. 18 of 13 April 2006 (approves Models and
Instructions for Completing Official Seed Analysis Bulletins and Seed Analysis Bulletins). **Diário Oficial da União**: Brasília, 19 April 2006. section 1, p.11-15.

CARBONELL, S.A.M. Methodology for selecting soya genotypes with seeds resistant to mechanical damage. Londrina. 1991. 103p. Dissertation (Master's Degree in Agronomy), State University of Londrina, 1991.

CARVALHO, N.M.; NAKAGAWA, J. Semente: ciência, tecnologia e produção. 4 ed. Jaboticabal: FUNEP, 2000. 588p.

CÔRREA-FERREIRA, B.S; KRZYZANNOWSKI, F.C; MINAMI, C.A. **Bedbugs and soya bean seed quality.** Seeds Series. Londrina: Embrapa Soja, 2009 (Embrapa Soja, Technical Circular, 67).

COSTA, N.P.; MESQUITA, C.M.; MAURINA, A.C.; FRANÇANETO, J.B.;
PEREIRA, J.E.; BORDINGNON, J.R.; KRZYZONOWSKI, F.C.; HENNING, A. A. Effect of mechanical harvesting of soya beans on the physical, physiological and chemical characteristics of the seeds at three Brazilian states. **Revista Brasileira de Sementes**, v.23, n.1, p. 140-145, 2001.

COSTA, N.P.; MESQUISTA, C.M. MAURINA, A.C. Physiological, physical and sanitary quality of soya bean seeds produced in Brazil. Revista Brasileira de Sementes, vol. 25, n° 1, p.128- 132,2003.

COSTG, P. NILTON . Seed health quality. In: França Neto, J. B.; Henning, A.A. Physiological and sanitary quality of soya beans. Londrina: Embrapa Soja. 1984.

DALL'GNOL, A. **O impacto da soja sobre a economia brasileira.**Informações técnicas para a agricultura. São Paulo, Máquinas Agrícolas Jacto, 2009.

FERREIRA, A.G. & BORGUETTI, F. **Germination**: from basic to applied. Porto Alegre: Artmed, 2004, 323p.

FILHO, J.M.; Seed Physiology of Cultivated Plants. Piracicaba, SP: FEALP, 2005.

PRÓ-SEMENTES FOUNDATION - Alexandre Levien - Seed certification manager.

FLOSS, E.L. **Physiology of cultivated plants: the study behind what you see**. 5. Ed. .-Passo Fundo: Ed. Universidade de Passo Fundo, 2011.

FRANÇA-NETO, J. B.; HENNING, A.A. Qualidade fisiológica da semente. Londrina: EMBRAPA/CNPSo, 2004. p.5-24. Technical Circular, 9.

FRANÇA-NETO, J. B.; HENNING, A.A. Qualidade fisiológica da semente. Londrina: EMBRAPA/CNPSo, 1894. p.5-24. Technical Circular, 9.

FREITAS, M. de C.M. et al. **The Soya Crop in Brazil.** ENCICLOPÉDIA BIOSFERA, Centro Científico Conhecer - Goiânia, vol.7, N.12; 2011 Pág.1

GALLO, D.; NAKANO, O.; SILVEIRA, NETO, S.; CARVALHO, R.P.L.;
BAPTISTA, G.C.; BERTI FILHO, E.; PARRA, J.R.P.; ZUCCHI, R.A.; ALVES, S.B.; VENDRAMIM, J.D.; MARCHINI, J.C.; LOPES, J.R.S.; OMOTO, C. *Entomologia Agrícola*. Piracicaba: FEALQ, 2002. 920 p.

GIOMO, G.S. Processing of coffee seeds (Coffea arabica L.) and effects on quality. Botucatu, 2003, 95 f., Thesis (Doctorate in agronomy), Universidade Federal Paulista.

HAMPTON, J.G. & TEKRONY, D.M. Accelerated aging test. In: Handbook of vigour test methods. Zurich: International Seed Testing Association, p.1- 10, 1995.

HENNING, A.A Sanitary quality of seeds. In: França Neto, J. B.; Henning, A.A. Physiological and sanitary quality of soya beans. Londrina: Embrapa Soja. 1984. P.25-39. (Embrapa Soya, Technical Circular 10).

KUENEMAN (1989) suggested using the "drop test" as a selection method for soya beans, given its use in seeds

KRZYZANOWSKI, F.C.; FRANÇA NETO , J. B; HENNING, AA.;COSTA,N.P. Soybean seed as a technology and basis for high yields - Seed series. Londrina: Embrapa soya, 2008[a]. 8p (Technical circular, 55)

KRZYZANOWSKI, F.C. **Ecological zoning of the state of Paraná for seed production of early soya cultivars.** Revista Brasileira de Sementes, Brasília, v.16, n.1, p.12-19, 1994.

KRZYZANOWSKI, F.C.; FRANÇA NETO , J. B; HENNING, AA.;COSTA,N.P. Soybean seed as a technology and basis for high yields - Seed series. Londrina: Embrapa soya, 1984a.

McDONALD JUNIOR, M.B. Vigour test subcommittee report. News Lett. Assoc. Proceeding of Association of Official Seed Analysts, Washington, v.54, n.1, p.37-40, 1980.

MARCOS FILHO, J; November A,D,L,C; Accelerated ageing test for soya beans. Scientia Agricola, v57, n3, p 473-482, 2001.

MARCOS FILHO, J.; CICERO, S. M.; SILVA, W. R. Evaluation of seed quality. Piracicaba: FEALQ, 1987. 230 p.

MARCOS, S.; MIELII, U. Axial-Flow, the new productivity champion, Available at . Accessed on 26/05/2003.

MIELEZRSKI, F.; SCHUCH, L.O.B.; PESKE, S.T.; PANOZZO, L.E.; PESKE, F.T.; CARVALHO, R.R. Individual performance and populations of hybrid rice plants as a function of seed physiological quality. Revista Brasileira de Sementes, v.30, n.3, p.86-94, 2008.

PAIVA, L.E.; MEDEIROS, S.F.; FRAGA, A.C. Processing of mechanically harvested maize seeds in cobs: effects

PAULSEN, M. R. Fracture resistance of soybean to compressive loading. Transaction of tche ASAE, v.21, n.6, p. 1210-1216, 1978.

PANIZZI,R.R.; SMITHJ.C.; PEREIRA,L.A.G.; YAMASHITA, J. Efeito de danos de *Piezodorus guildinni* (Westwood, 1837) no rendimento e qualidade da soja. In: Seminário nacional de pesquisa de soja. londrina,

1978. **anais**... londrina, embrapa-cnpso, 1979. v. 2 p.59-78.

PESKE, S.T.; ROSENTHAL, M.D.; ROTA, G.R.M. Seeds: Scientific and technological foundations. 3ª edition. Pelotas: Editora rua Pelotas, 2012. 573p.

RONDON, E.V. Biomass production and growth of Schizolobium amazonicum (Huber) Ducke trees under different spacings in a forest region. Revista Árvore, Viçosa, v.26, n.5, p.573-576, 2002

SILVA, S. S.; BERNARDO, D. C. R.; SANTOS, A. C.; SALAZAR, G. T.: Estimation of the soya production function in Brazil from 1994 to 2003. Congress Proceedings. XLIII Sober Congress in Ribeirão Preto. São Paulo, 2005.

TEKRONY, D.M. Accelerated aging. In: VAN DE CENTER, H.A. (Ed.). Seed vigour testing seminar. Copenhagen: The International Seed Testing Association, p. 53-72, 1995.

TOLEDO , F.F.; MARCOS FILHO, J. Manual de sementes- tecnologia da produção. São Paulo: Ed. Agronomica ceres, 2001. 224 p.

VAUGHAN, C.E. Quality assurance techniques - the chlorox test In: SHORT COURSE FOR SEEDSMEN, 1982, State College. Proceedings ... State College: Mississippi Seed Technology Laboratory, 1982. p.117-118

Milton Keynes UK
Ingram Content Group UK Ltd.
UKHW011146010424
440421UK00001B/334